DETROIT PUBLIC LIBRARY
3 5674 00847836 5

W9-CKI-975

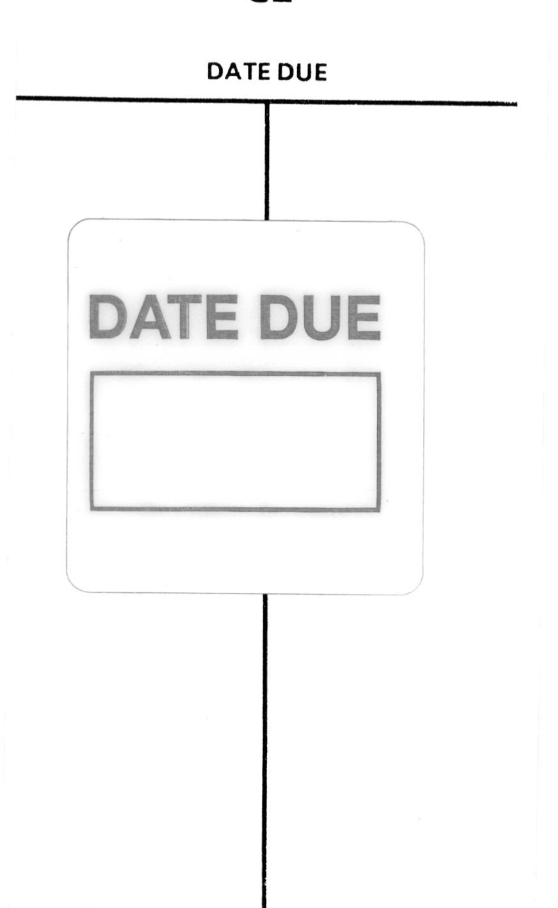
DATE DUE

AROUND THE YEAR

HENRY Z. WALCK, INCORPORATED

AROUND
the
YEAR
TASHA
TUDOR

Library of Congress Catalog Card Number: 60-7419
Printed in the United States of America

To

a certain person
for whom this country
in the hills beyond
has a special meaning

January brings us

coasting,

Taffy pulls and apple roasting.

T. Tudor
1957

Chill February

brings the day,

When hearts and flowers

we give away.

March promises

the hope of spring,

In swampy places peepers sing.

T. Tudor

April sees the birds return,

T. Tudor

Scatters showers

on leaf and fern.

May brings us

armfuls of delight,

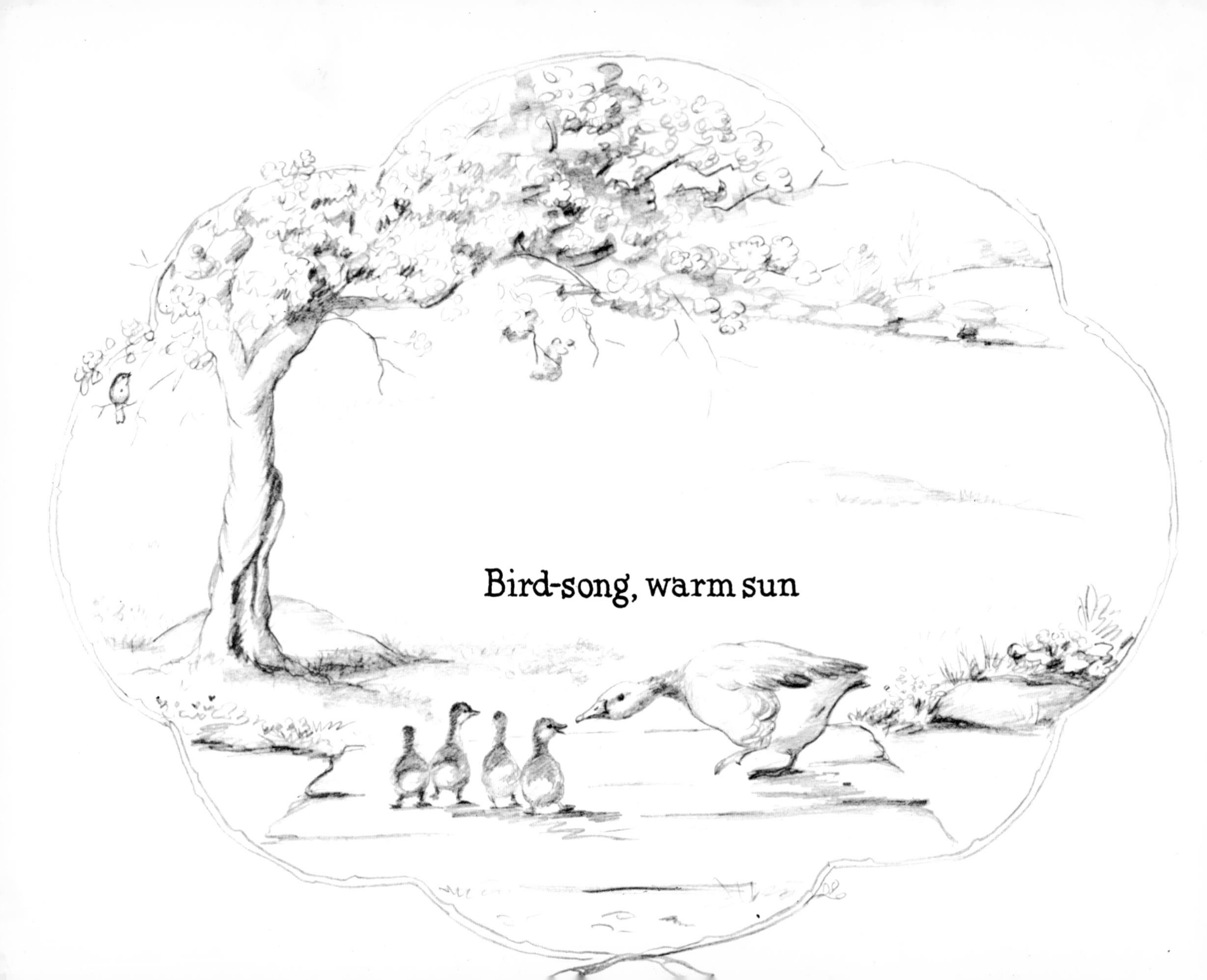

Bird-song, warm sun

and gardens bright.

In June comes

summer's longest day,

Now meadows smell

of new-mown hay.

Hot July brings picnic joys,

Firecrackers for girls and boys.

In August

swallows southward fly,

Summer's waning, fall is nigh.

September brings the Country Fair,

Falling leaves,

crisp autumn air.

October brings us

Halloween,

When witches, ghosts

and spooks are seen.

November brings

good skating weather,

Thanksgiving gathers us together.

T. Tudor
1957

December brings
THE NIGHT BEFORE CHRISTMAS
Noel

glad Christmas cheer,

May joy be yours

T. Tudor 1957
Around the Year.

T. Tudor